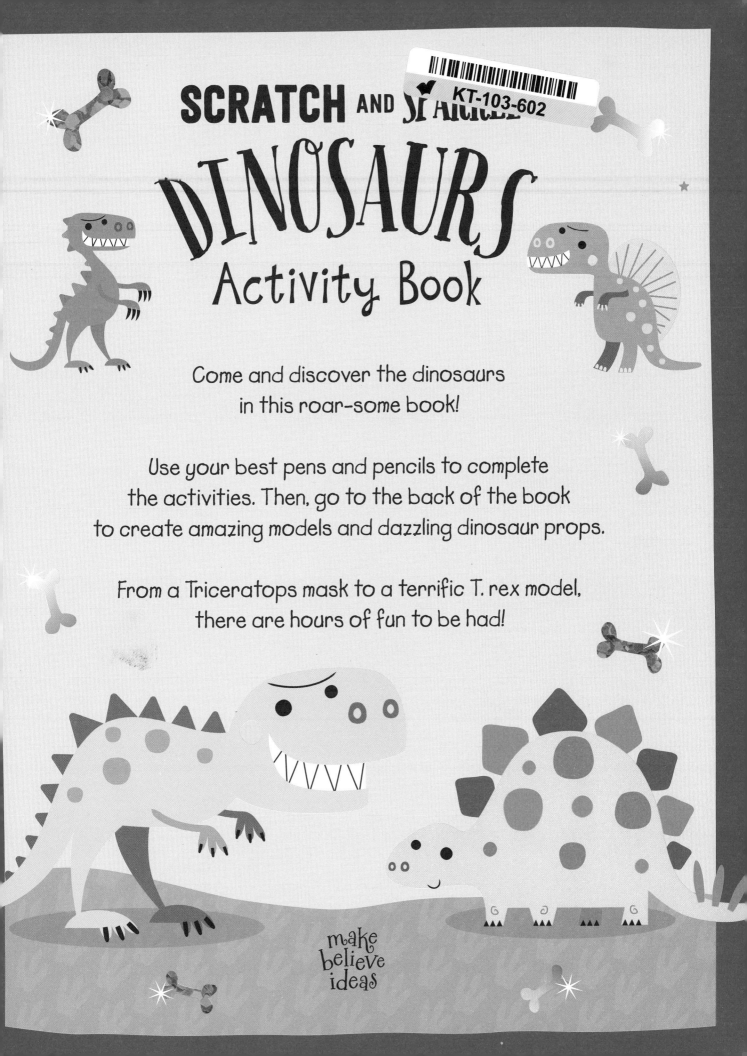

SCRATCH AND SPARKLE

DINOSAURS
Activity Book

Come and discover the dinosaurs
in this roar-some book!

Use your best pens and pencils to complete
the activities. Then, go to the back of the book
to create amazing models and dazzling dinosaur props.

From a Triceratops mask to a terrific T. rex model,
there are hours of fun to be had!

make
believe
ideas

How to use your scratch-off pages:

At the back of the book, there are dinosaur props for you to press out, create and wear. Look for the call-out on each page to see what you can make.

1. Use the scratcher to give your props sparkling details.

2. Gently press out the shapes.

3. Finish the props with ribbon, glue and some help from an adult!

Triceratops mask
See page 4

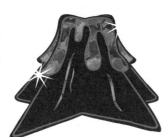

3-D volcano
See page 7

Pterodactyl gliders
See page 15

Dinosaur model
See page 27

Pop-up card
See page 28

Prehistoric pals

Allosaurus
(AL-oh-SORE-us)

Diplodocus
(dih-PLOD-uh-kus)

Elasmosaurus
(el-LAZ-moe-SORE-us)

Ankylosaurus
(AN-kee-lo-SORE-us)

Brachiosaurus
(BRACK-ee-oh-SORE-us)

Kronosaurus
(KRON-oh-SORE-us)

Liopleurodon
(LIE-oh-PLOO-ro-don)

Parasaurolophus
(pa-ra-SORE-OH-lo-fus)

Lambeosaurus
(LAM-bee-oh-SORE-us)

Pterodactyl
(TER-uh-DAK-til)

Quetzalcoatlus
(KET-zal-co-AT-lus)

Stegosaurus
(STEG-oh-SORE-us)

Spinosaurus
(SPINE-oh-SORE-us)

Pterosaur
(TER-uh-SORE)

Velociraptor
(vel-OSS-ee-rap-tor)

Triceratops
(tri-SERR-ah-tops)

Tsintaosaurus
(CHING-dow-SORE-us)

T. rex
(TEE-rex)

3

Who's who?

Look at the pictures. Write the letters to answer the questions.

Who has a gold tooth?	Who is the smallest?	Who is wearing a top hat?	Who is wearing red boots?
○	○	○	○ ....

A

B

C

D

E

MAKE YOUR OWN TRICERATOPS MASK

1. Use your scratcher to add dazzling details to the mask.

2. Gently press out the mask shape and eye holes.

3. Ask an adult to help you thread some ribbon through the holes and tie it around your head.

4

Talent show

The dinosaurs are having a talent show! Use colour
to finish the patterns and discover what they can do.

Volcano view

Search the scene for the things below.
✓ the box when you find them.

- [ ] 5 sparks
- [ ] 4 Pterodactyl
- [ ] 3 eggs
- [ ] 6 dragonflies
- [ ] 1 Stegosaurus
- [ ] 2 Lambeosaurus

MAKE YOUR OWN 3-D VOLCANO

1. Use your scratcher to add sizzling details to the volcano.

2. Gently press out the shapes and open the slots.

3. Then, slot the volcano together to make it stand up.

Dinosaur dinners

The dinosaurs love a fearsome feast.
Draw a tasty dinner on the plate.

Follow the lines to see what
Ankylosaurus Annie is eating.

Copy and colour the cupcake. Use the grid to guide you.

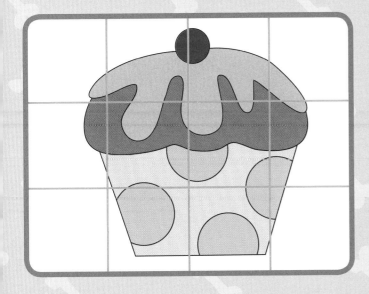

Circle the one that doesn't belong in each group.

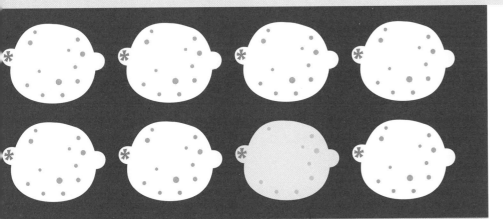

Going dotty

Join the dots to finish the picture.
Then, colour it in.

Triceratops trail

Find a path through the cave
to help Triceratops Tia get home.
Collect all four rubies along the way.

Start

Finish

Bart

Elsa

Lily

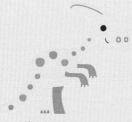

Penny

Stuart

Val

Baby boom

Search the grid for the baby dinosaur names.
Names can go down or across.

v	s	b	a	r	t	d	e	a
n	r	s	l	f	s	o	s	t
s	l	y	s	t	b	i	y	i
e	e	c	l	s	p	s	o	s
e	l	p	e	n	n	y	e	t
l	s	y	s	a	d	o	s	u
a	a	p	e	l	v	a	r	a
s	e	s	s	r	a	s	p	r
r	s	r	l	i	l	y	s	t

Colour in the daddy
dino and baby Vince.

I'm walking here!

Look at the footprints and match them to the dinosaur prints below.
✓ the boxes for every footprint you can see.

Which dinosaur hasn't been here?
Write the letter.

Dinosaur detective

Which dinosaur fits the picture clues?
Circle the answer to each sum.

purple tail + pink and purple spots + two feet =

blue and orange spots + plates + spiked tail =

sharp teeth + green spots + blue frill =

Summer break

The Pterodactyl are going on holiday!
Use the key to see where they're going.

A	B	C	D	E	F	G	H	I	J	K	L	M
N	O	P	Q	R	S	T	U	V	W	X	Y	Z

→ D _ _ E _ _
  _ I _ _ N

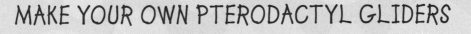

→ _ O _ T _ _
  R _ S _ _

MAKE YOUR OWN PTERODACTYL GLIDERS

1. Use your scratcher to add glittering details to the pterodactyl gliders. Then, shade the reverse sides.

2. Gently press out the shapes and the thin slits.

3. Slot the feet onto the tails of the gliders. Then, slide the wings into place.

4. Slide paperclips onto the noses of the gliders. Finally, watch them take flight!

Sea scenes

Help Elasmosaurus Elsa find a path through the tangled seaweed to her friend Kronosaurus Karl.

Start

Finish

CHALLENGE MODE:
Can you find your way through the maze in under thirty seconds?

Can you find the creature with this silhouette?

Colour the scene.

Trace the lines to reveal who is lurking in the deep.

17

Dinosaur disco

Draw lines to match the dancing pairs.

Draw Tsintaosaurus Chad a partner.
Use the grid as a guide.

Dino maths

Write down the correct order of
dinosaurs from the smallest to the tallest.

A   B   C   D

smallest .... tallest

How many eggs can you count?
Write the answer.

......

Who has the most spots? Write the totals in the roundels,
and then circle the one with the most.

A   B   C

....

Little dino lost

T. rex Terry is lost!
Can you find him?

Crazy colours

Colour the crazy scene! Use the key as a guide.

1 = pink
2 = red
3 = green
4 = yellow
5 = orange
6 = blue
7 = purple
8 = brown

Carnivore camping

The dinosaurs have gone camping.
Search the scene for the things below.
✓ the boxes as you find them.

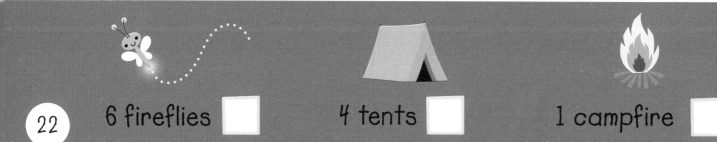

6 fireflies ☐   4 tents ☐   1 campfire ☐

1 guitar ☐   3 Allosaurus ☐   2 Pterosaur ☐

Jurassic grid

Search the grid for the patterns below.
Put a tick in the box when you've found them.

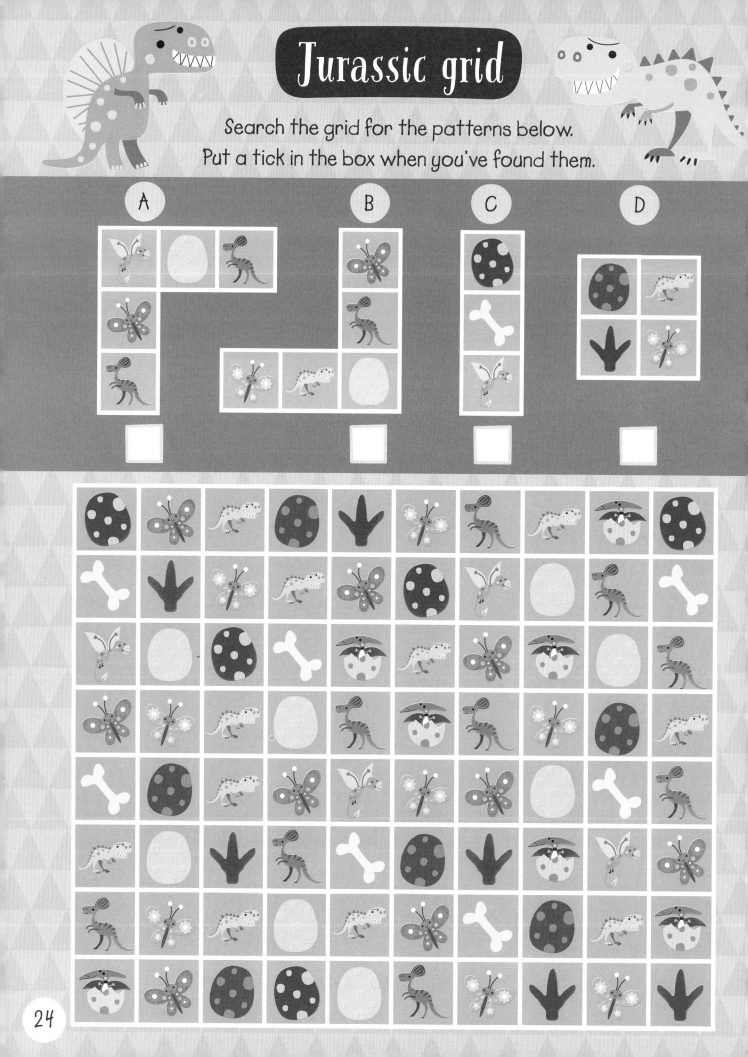

Dinosaur dig

Colour the sections with bones in them to unearth this dinosaur discovery.

Air cadets

The Flight Academy is putting on a show!
Find and circle eight differences between the scenes.

Close-up

The dinosaurs are on a photoshoot. Draw lines to match each dinosaur with the correct close-up.

MAKE YOUR OWN DINOSAUR MODEL

1. Use your scratcher to add unique details to the dinosaur model and footprints.

2. Gently press out the model and footprints. Then, open the slots and fold along the creases.

3. Tape the head of the dinosaur down over the flap. Then, lay out the footprints to finish.

Home, sweet home

Help Bertha back to her nest.
You can only step on the orange footprints!

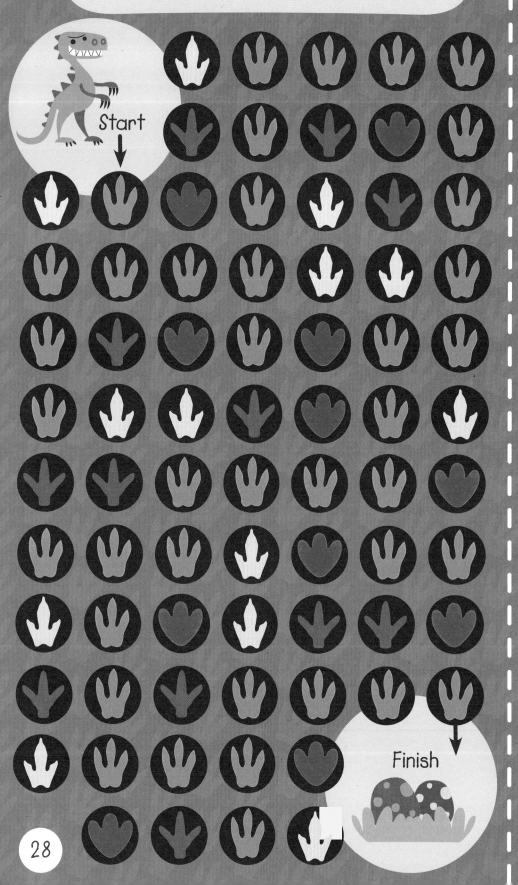

Start

Finish

CREATE A POP-UP CARD

1. Use your scratcher to add egg-cellent details to the card.

2. Gently press out the card and open the slots at the top and bottom of the egg shape.

3. Fold along the crease.

4. Finally, push the egg forwards to finish.